QUICK START! draw, PAINT, STICK

PETs

Isobel Lundie

Artist

Isobel Lundie studied illustration and animation at Kingston University in 2015.
She has a special interest in interactive books for children.

How to use this book

Follow the easy, numbered instructions. Simple step-by-step stages enable budding young artists to create their own lively works of art.

What you will need

On each page you will find a list of basic art materials. Some crafts involve the use of scissors, so adult supervision is advised.

Published in Great Britain in MMXVIII by Scribblers, an imprint of
The Salariya Book Company Ltd
25 Marlborough Place,
Brighton BN1 1UB
www.salariya.com

© The Salariya Book Company Ltd
MMXVIII

ISBN-13: 978-1-912006-16-8

1 3 5 7 9 8 6 4 2

A CIP catalogue record for this book is available from the British Library.

Printed and bound in Malaysia.

Visit
www.salariya.com
for our online catalogue and **free** fun stuff.

Contents

Crayon Horse

It is much simpler to draw animals shape by shape. This technique uses pencil crayons to create rich colours by colouring, patterning and scribbling!

You will need:
- Pencil crayons
- Drawing paper

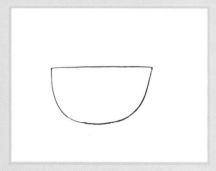

1 Use a black pencil crayon to draw this shape for the horse's body.

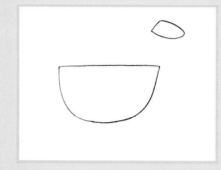

2 Next, draw in the shape for the horse's head.

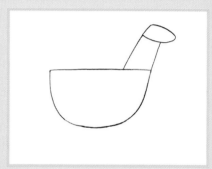

3 Draw in the horse's neck to join the body to the head.

4 Add four bent legs and a long swishy tail.

5 Draw the horse's tummy and saddle, and a mane.

6 Finally, add small details like the hooves, eyes and mouth.

Use a grey pencil crayon to colour in the horse's body.

Draw in a meadow for the horse to run in. You could add a farm house and mountains... or make up your own background.

Use a yellow pencil crayon to colour in the horse's saddle.

5

Inky Cat

Ink can be very messy! Make sure you use a palette to mix your inks.

You will need:

- Coloured crayons
- Drawing paper
- Coloured inks

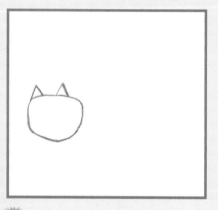

1 Use an orange crayon to draw the head and ears.

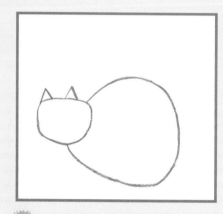

2 Draw a big round shape for the cat's body.

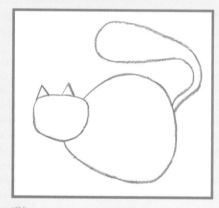

3 Now add its big swooshy tail!

4 Draw in both front legs, and one back leg.

5 Use a black crayon to add the cat's stripes!

6 Draw in its eyes and mouth. Use a pink crayon for its ears and nose.

Mix together yellow and orange ink to colour your cat. Leave the eyes and face white.

Draw in a g... your cat to explore. Add the grass texture using a green crayon.

Once the ink is dry, draw on the cat's whiskers!

Crayon in some leaves and use ink to colour them.

7

Tissue Paper Dog

Remember to keep your hands clean when you are tearing your tissue paper.

1 Use a black felt-tip pen to draw the dog's head.

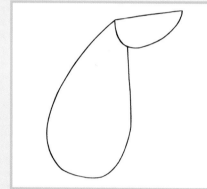

2 Draw a big teardrop shape for the dog's body.

3 Next, draw in both front legs and one back leg.

4 Draw two big loopy ears and a curved tail.

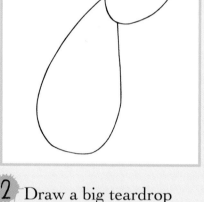

5 Add the eye, nose, mouth and tongue.

6 Colour in the ears. Tear and glue on pieces of orange tissue paper for the body.

Tear green strips of tissue
paper to make leaves.

Tear a thin strip of
pink tissue paper to
glue in place for the
dog's tongue.

Use a felt-tip pen to
draw three black spots
on the dog's back.

When the glue has dried,
you can draw over some of
the black lines to clean up
your collage.

9

Chalk Hamster

There are loads of different ways to create marks using chalks! Try smudging colours with your finger to blend them.

You will need:
- Black paper
- Coloured chalks
- White chalk

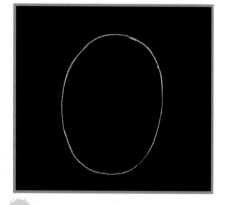

1 Use white chalk to draw a big oval.

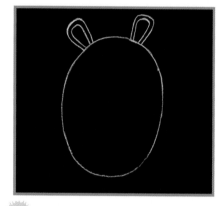

2 Draw in two lines for each ear.

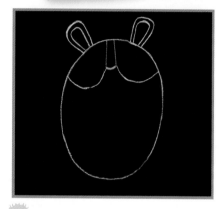

3 Next, draw in the cheeks and add a pink nose.

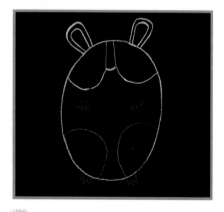

4 Draw the hands and feet in red chalk, and the legs in brown.

5 Add small details like the eyes and mouth and the shape of the tummy.

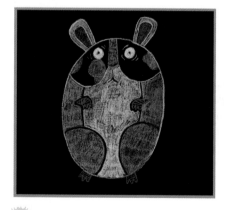

6 Finally, use your chalks to colour in your hamster!

Use brown coloured chalk for the hamster's fur. Scribble in the same direction to create a fur texture.

Draw in the hamster's wheel and blankets using bright coloured chalks.

11

Painted Lizard

Add plenty of water to your paint to make different watery colours for your lizard.

You will need:
- Poster paints
- Paintbrushes
- White cartridge paper

1 Use watery green paint for the lizard's body.

2 Use yellow-green paint for its bobbly legs.

3 Use white paint for its eyes, teeth and spots.

4 Use a fine brush to paint the eyes and mouth.

5 Use darker green paint on the eyelids.

6 Finally, use light yellow paint for its spikes.

Using watery colours can help you to create different tones.

You could paint a background for your lizard.

Create a two-tone effect for the feet: first use a watery yellow colour and allow to dry. Then cover half of the foot with a watery green.

Paint lots of fat green bushes. Once dry, use a smaller brush to add little leaves using a darker shade of green.

13

Handprint Tortoise

Have great fun creating messy handprints,
then draw onto your prints to make a tortoise!

You will need:

- Poster paints
- Large paintbrush
- Coloured paper
- Black felt-tip pen
- Scissors
- PVA glue

1 Paint your hand with poster paint and press it down firmly onto paper.

2 Mix grey poster paint for the tortoise's shell. Paint a semicircle.

3 Use a black felt-tip pen to draw a pattern all over the shell (as shown).

4 Next, draw an eye, nostril and mouth.

5 Then add his knees, scales and toes.

6 Cut around your tortoise, then glue him onto coloured paper.

Make some
fingerprint
leaves for your
tortoise to eat.

You could start off by
painting the palm of
your hand grey and
your fingers green,
to save you from
having to paint the
shell on later.

Here are some more
handprint animal
ideas for you to print
and paint.

Dog

Cat

15

Paper Cup Mice

You will need:
- Pencil
- Paper cups
- Poster paints
- Paintbrush
- Cartridge paper

Get drawing, painting and sticking with these cute little paper cup mice!

1 Paint a paper cup light grey all over.

2 Paint on a white tummy and a dark grey face shape.

3 Paint and cut out two ears and a tail.

4 Stick both ears to the top of the cup and the tail to one side.

5 Using a small brush, paint on pink paws and white eyes.

6 Add black felt-tip dots to draw on the eyes. Draw whiskers and small hairs on the face.

16

It's a good idea to hold the ears in place while the glue dries so they don't fall off!

These mice are different colours. Try out your own ideas – big ears, small ears, or perhaps even draw in a woolly scarf?

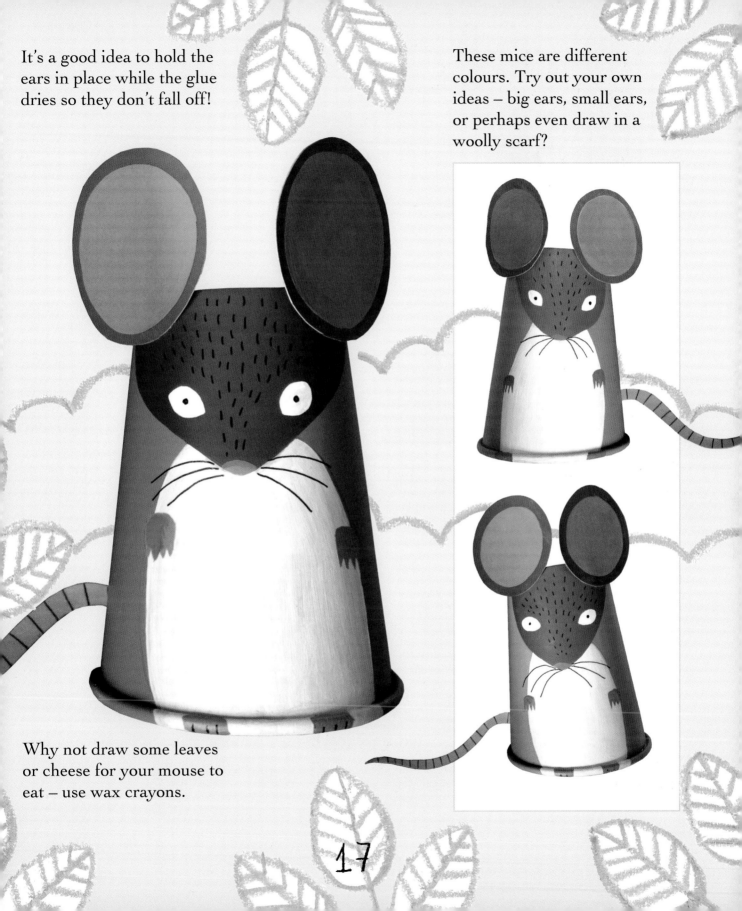

Why not draw some leaves or cheese for your mouse to eat – use wax crayons.

17

Cat Pebble

Try to collect the flattest, smoothest pebbles you can as these will be easiest to paint on. Bigger pebbles will also be easier to paint!

You will need:
- Coloured pencil
- Pebbles
- Poster paints
- Paintbrushes
- White paper

1 Choose a small oval pebble and a large squarish one. Paint both white.

2 Cut paper triangles for the ears and cut a long tail shape. Stick onto the pebble.

3 Pencil in the cat's face, legs, tummy and stripes.

4 Paint the cat's stripes using grey poster paint and a small brush.

5 Add small touches of pink poster paint to the ears and nose.

6 Paint in the remaining details like the eyes, paws and mouth.

18

Each cat will look different
depending on the shape and
size of the pebble used. Try
out different shapes!

19

Folded Paper Fish

Make sure you use paper that is thin enough to fold easily.

You will need:

- Poster paints
- Paintbrushes
- Square of white paper
- Black felt-tip pen
- Pencil

1 Paint one side of the paper blue. Leave to dry. Fold in half and crease.

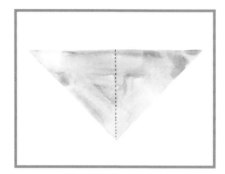

2 Unfold your paper. Now fold and crease the other diagonal.

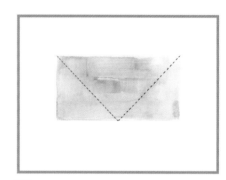

3 Unfold it. Now fold and crease into a rectangle (as shown). Unfold again.

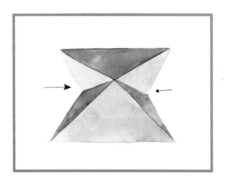

4 Now, push the side folds inwards to make a triangle shape.

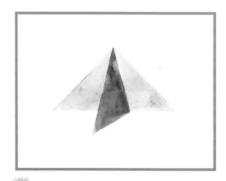

5 Fold one front flap over to make a fin.

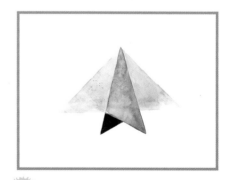

6 Fold the other flap over it to make another fin. Flip over your fish!

When you've finished, why not paint some seaweed for your fish to swim around?

Pencil in your fish design, then use paint to colour it. Use a black felt-tip pen for the finishing touches.

You could even add bright yellow or red stripes.

If you splat watery blue paint onto wet pink paint you will create this nice splotchy effect.

Printed Snake

This colourful snake looks great and is fun to make too. Ask an adult to cut your potato!

You will need:
- Poster paints
- Black felt-tip pen
- White cartridge paper
- small potato cut in half and a chip

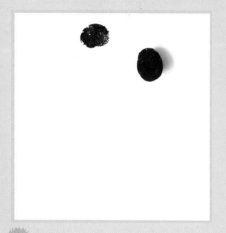

1 Dip half a potato in red paint, then press onto paper.

2 Use a potato chip shape to print the body.

3 Using a small brush, paint in yellow stripes.

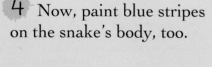

4 Now, paint blue stripes on the snake's body, too.

5 Use a black felt-tip pen to draw in more stripes.

6 Now paint a white circle for the eye and add a black dot. Draw a mouth.

It's a good idea to cut your potato the night before. This gives it time to dry out, which is better for printing.

Halve a potato and paint the flat side purple. Print it three times to make leaves. Once dry, use a black felt-tip pen to add details.

Make sure to give your snake some sharp teeth!

23

Coloured Paper Sausage Dog

You will need:

- Coloured cartridge paper
- PVA glue
- Scissors
- Pencil
- Black felt-tip pen

Choose paper that is thick enough to stand up when folded, but not too thick to cut out small details.

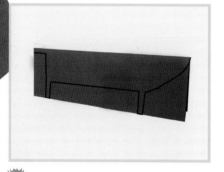

1 Fold an A4 piece of brown cartridge paper in half. Now draw a simple outline of a sausage dog.

2 Ask an adult to help you carefully cut around the dog-shaped outline.

3 Fold a small piece of dark brown paper in half. Draw a tear shaped ear.

4 Ask an adult to help you cut the shape out. Glue the ears in place.

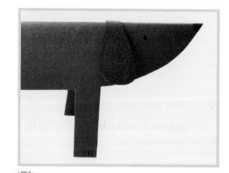

5 Use a black felt-tip pen to add dots for the eyes and to draw the nose and paws.

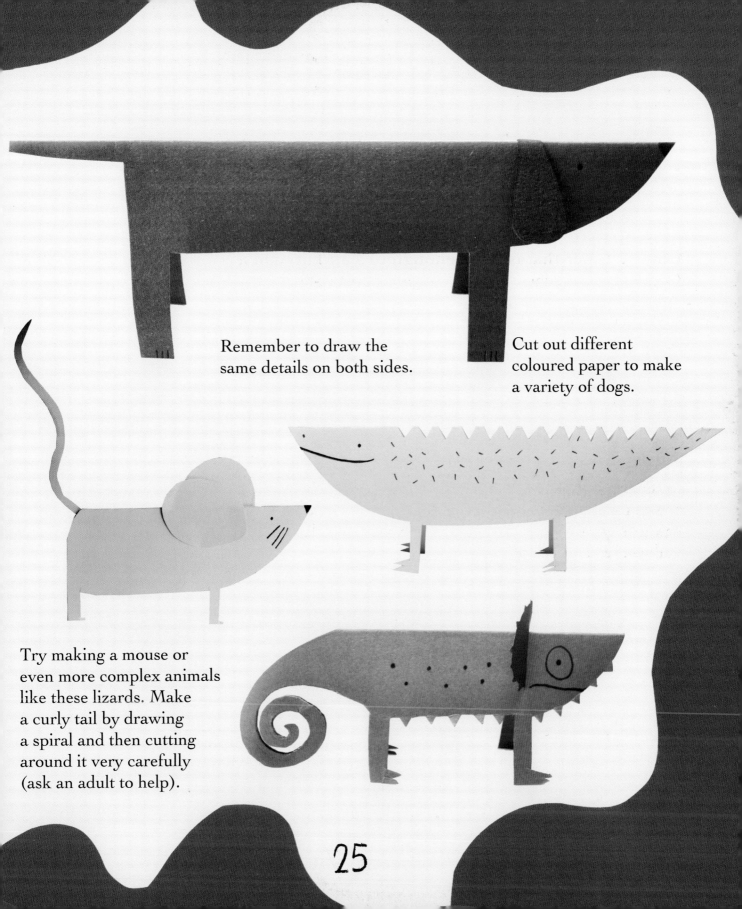

Remember to draw the
same details on both sides.

Cut out different
coloured paper to make
a variety of dogs.

Try making a mouse or
even more complex animals
like these lizards. Make
a curly tail by drawing
a spiral and then cutting
around it very carefully
(ask an adult to help).

Torn Paper Zebra Finch

Make sure that the paper you use is thin enough to rip easily.

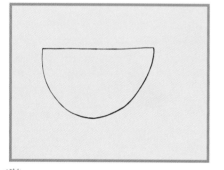

1 Use a pencil to draw a big semicircle on scrap paper.

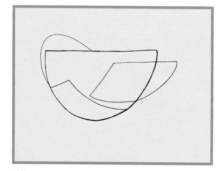

2 Draw on the bird's wing, head shape and tummy.

3 Draw in its beak and three curved tail feathers.

4 Place the outline onto grey coloured paper and create an indent shape of the body by pressing down on the drawing with a pencil.

5 Repeat on different coloured papers for the different body parts. Then tear out the indents.

6 Stick them down in the shape of the bird. Use a black felt-tip and small torn pieces of coloured paper for details.

Try making wings
for your zebra finch
so it can fly!

Tear some coloured
paper to make green
leaves and brown
branches for the
background.

Use leftover
paper dots from
the hole punch
to create perfect
round markings!

27

Collage Fish

You will need:
- Coloured paper
- Newspapers
- Magazines
- Scissors
- PVA glue

Make sure you collect a variety of coloured craft papers and magazine cuttings, as th...

colla gee fish

1 Cut an oval out of orange paper. Glue onto some plain paper.

2 Cut a fan shaped tail out of grey magazine pages.

3 Cut and stick on four fins using the same paper.

4 Cut long strips of newspaper to stick on in a criss-cross pattern.

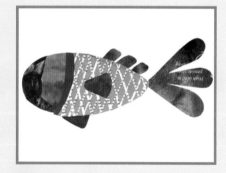

5 Glue on a head shape and a dorsal fin.

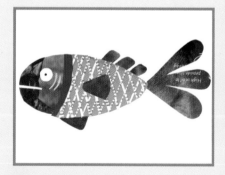

6 Finally, cut out an eye, mouth and gills. Stick onto your fish's head.

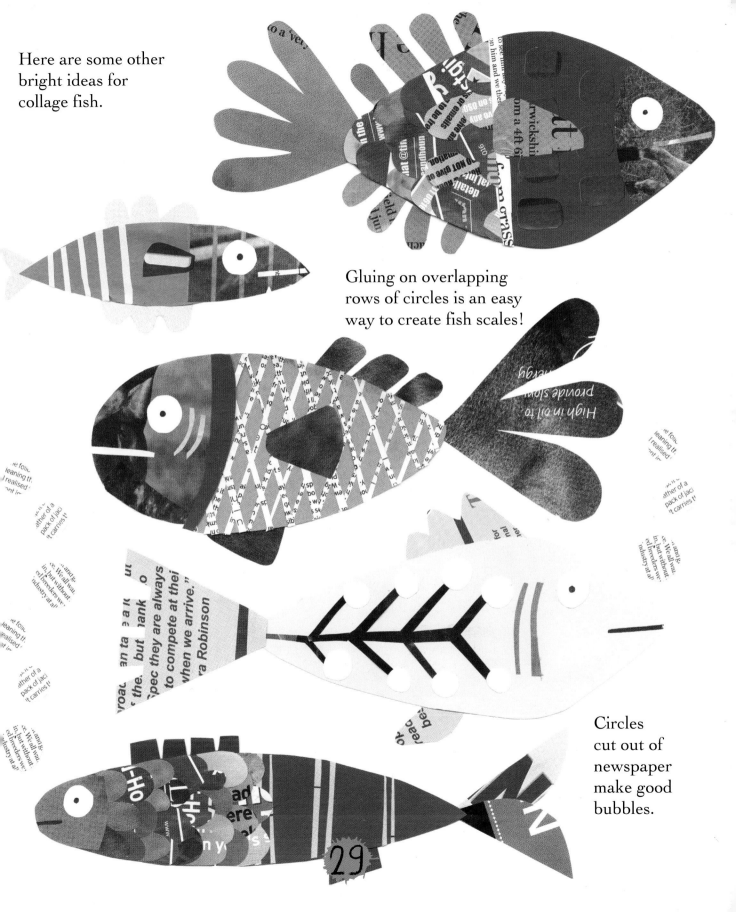

Here are some other bright ideas for collage fish.

Gluing on overlapping rows of circles is an easy way to create fish scales!

Circles cut out of newspaper make good bubbles.

29

Mosaic Chamaeleon

You will need:
- Scissors
- PVA glue
- Coloured papers
- Black paper
- Pencil

Make sure an adult can help you before starting this project as there is a lot of cutting!

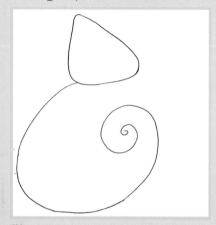

1 Use a pencil to draw the head shape and spiral.

2 Draw a big eye and legs. Add another line for the tail.

3 Draw in more details like the mouth and scales.

4 Scribble white crayon over the back of your drawing. Place it on black paper. Pencil over the lines to transfer them.

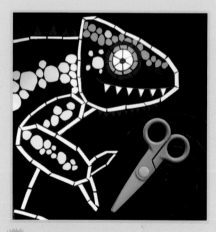

5 Now, using the white crayon guide lines, start to stick down tiles of paper mosaic.

6 Glue on lots of coloured paper mosaics until your chamaeleon is finished!

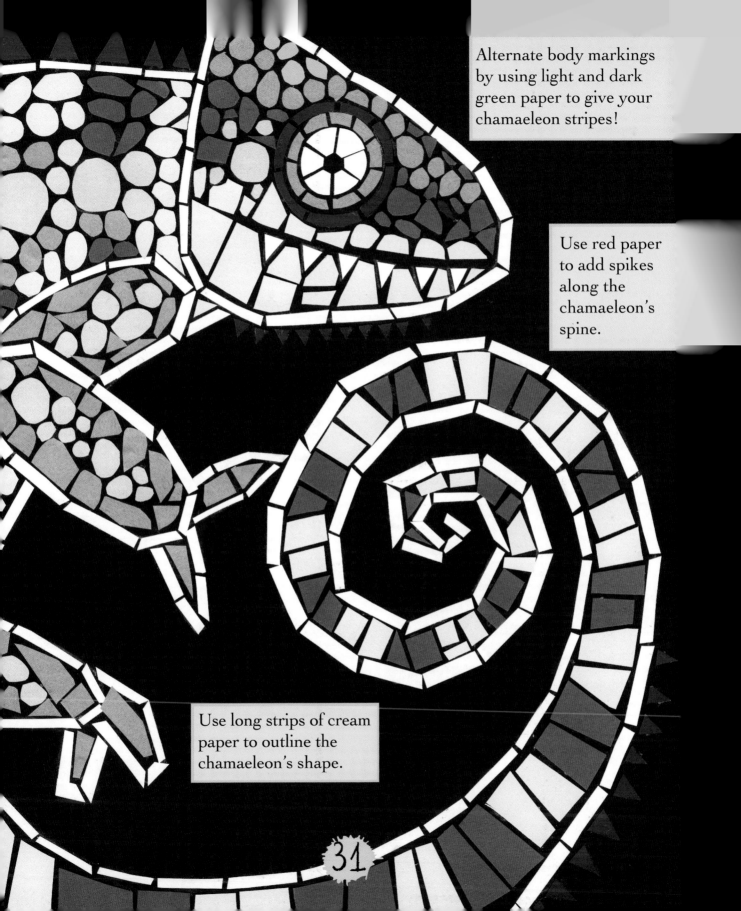

Alternate body markings by using light and dark green paper to give your chamaeleon stripes!

Use red paper to add spikes along the chamaeleon's spine.

Use long strips of cream paper to outline the chamaeleon's shape.

Glossary

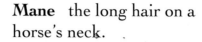

Collage an artwork made from various materials pasted onto a surface.

Dorsal fin the triangular fin found on the backs of many types of fish.

Gills the slits on fishes' necks through which they breathe.

Mane the long hair on a horse's neck.

Mosaic an artwork made from small coloured pieces of glass or other materials.

Palette the container in which an artist mixes different colours of paints.

Texture the look and feel of the surface of a material or picture.

Zebra finch a kind of bird commonly found in Central Australia.

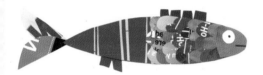

Index